The Clown who couldn't Smile

STARTER

Alison Chaplin

AUTHOR
Alison Chaplin

EDITOR
Steven Carruthers

ASSISTANT EDITOR
Roanne Davis

SERIES DESIGNER
Anna Oliwa/Heather Sanneh

DESIGNER
Rachael Hammond

ILLUSTRATIONS
Woody

COVER ARTWORK
Woody

Text © 2000 Alison Chaplin
© 2000 Scholastic Ltd

Designed using Adobe Pagemaker

Published by Scholastic Ltd,
Villiers House,
Clarendon Avenue,
Leamington Spa,
Warwickshire CV32 5PR

1 2 3 4 5 6 7 8 9 0   0 1 2 3 4 5 6 7 8 9

British Library Cataloguing-in-Publication Data. A catalogue record for this book is available from the British Library.

ISBN 0-439-01747-5

ACKNOWLEDGEMENTS

First performed in Manchester by participants on the 'Drama and Theatre Workshop' in August 1997. Many thanks to them for their suggestions of script changes and for their enthusiastic performances!

For permission to give a performance of this play at which an admission charge is made, please contact the Editorial Department, Educational Books, Scholastic Limited, Villiers House, Clarendon Avenue, Leamington Spa. Warks. CV32 5PR. You do not need to seek permission if you do not charge an entry fee for the performance. Performing licences must be applied for prior to beginning rehearsals.

Fees are £10.00 per performance for a paying audience of up to 200 people and £15.00 per performance for paying audiences of 200 people or over.

Alison Chaplin is the drama consultant for the Borough of Stockport and manager of 'Arts on the Move', a company specializing in providing a range of drama and theatre services. For information call 0161 881 0868.

CONTENTS LIST

INTRODUCTION

USING THIS BOOK

The aim of this Scholastic performance play is to provide teachers with the appropriate resources to read, rehearse and perform a short play. The book enables teachers and children to understand the process of interpreting scripts and the approaches needed for successful rehearsals and performances. From providing pre-rehearsal support to supplying linking reading and writing tasks, the book is structured in a way that assumes no prior knowledge of script work and no previous experience of staging performances, leading those involved through the process in easy-to-follow stages.

WORKSHOP SESSIONS

Workshop sessions are provided to help the teacher introduce the children to the concept of drama. The sessions help the children to:

- read and understand playscripts
- explore the implicit themes and issues within the play
- appreciate character development
- learn the skills required for performance.

Each session is structured to approach a different aspect of working with a playscript, using methods that are both practical and enjoyable.

PLAYSCRIPT

The playscript is organized in a simple-to-follow format, complete with full stage directions and scene changes. At the beginning of the script, following the cast list, is a set of brief character outlines that provide an indication of behavioural traits and help the children to understand how each role should be performed. Most of the plays in the *Performance Plays* series are simple to stage and require little in the way of make-up, costume or setting.

PRODUCTION SUPPORT

The production support notes provide practical advice to support teachers from the beginning to the end of the performance process, including holding auditions; structuring rehearsals; simple and effective staging, props, costumes and make-up; and finally, presenting professional 'curtain calls'.

The ideas have arisen from the author's own experience of directing the play and are thus informed by a knowledge of what has worked with children in practice. However, they are not intended to be prescriptive and if teachers feel that they have the resources, time and skills to create more elaborate staging and costumes, or to approach the performance in a different way, then they should feel free to do so!

LITERACY SUPPORT

The literacy support notes at the end of the book are directly linked to the requirements of the National Literacy Strategy *Framework for Teaching*. They provide suggestions for supportive tasks, organized under the headings of 'Story', 'Characters', 'Theme', 'Working with playscript layout' and 'Performance-related tasks'. Again, these are not prescriptive, but aim to provide teachers with examples of how the playscript can be used to generate structured literacy work.

The unique aspect of these *Performance Plays* is that their contents can be utilized in a number of different ways: as a simple reading resource, to provide a basis for literacy tasks, to introduce children to the concept of performance drama, or to produce a full-scale school play. Readers should feel free to employ the book in any way that meets their needs. However, the most important approach for anyone using this play is to be flexible, enthusiastic and to be prepared to 'have a go'!

GUIDANCE FOR WORKING WITH SCRIPTS

If the children have no previous experience of script work, it is suggested that you lead them through the following simple drama process in order to familiarize them with the style and concept of a scripted performance.

Ask the children (in their classroom places) to find a partner and instruct them to hold a conversation with him or her. It could be about anything – the television programmes they watched the night before, their favourite books, what they did during the school holidays, and so on. Allow these conversations to run for about a minute and then ask them to stop talking.

Now ask the children within each pair to label themselves 'A' and 'B'. Tell them that they must hold the conversation again, but advise them that this time 'B' cannot respond until 'A' has finished talking (or until 'A' has finished a sentence, if 'A' is going on for too long). Insist that the children adhere to this procedure for speaking and responding, as this forms the basis for most scripted formats.

Allow these structured conversations to run for

about a minute, then ask the children to stop talking. Invite them to give feedback on the type of conversations they had and, on the board, write their statements and responses in the form of an 'A said' and 'B said' structure:

A said: ....
B said: ....

Record just a couple of lines from each conversation, to show the children how these conversations can be recorded. Ask them to suggest how their second conversations differed from their original ones. Answers should include: the speakers had names ('A' and 'B'), that they could only speak when the other person had finished speaking, that the conversations were not as natural, and that they had to think more about what they said and how they responded to their partners.

Now ask the children to join with another pair to make a four. (Odd numbers or unequal groups are also acceptable.) Ask them to hold an initial unstructured conversation with each other about a subject of your choosing and leave these to run for about a minute. Then ask the children to label themselves 'A', 'B', 'C' and 'D' (match letters of the alphabet with the numbers in each group accordingly) and to hold the same conversation, imposing the same restriction as before: while someone in the group is talking, no one else can speak. Tell the children that they do not necessarily have to join in the conversation in alphabetical order.

Invite their feedback about these conversations. Again, ask for comments on how the second discussions differed from the first. Record part of a structured conversation on the board, using 'A', 'B',

'C' and 'D' to indicate who speaks which line.

Inform the children that this is how plays are structured – they are written records of people speaking to each other, having conversations or discussions – and that the names of the character speaking is indicated at the beginning of each line of dialogue.

Further practice for the children could include:

● recording their conversations in script form, using the 'A' and 'B' or 'A', 'B', 'C', 'D' format

● devising and writing original conversations, using the 'A' and 'B' or 'A', 'B', 'C', 'D' format

● lifting a section of dialogue from a familiar story and rewriting it in scripted form

● rewriting their own conversations, using names instead of letters of the alphabet

● improvising a scene (such as someone buying an item in a shop), recording it using a tape recorder or Dictaphone, then replaying the recording for them to transpose into a written script.

The main aim is to enable children to appreciate that a playscript is simply dialogue, conversations, discussions or verbal statements written down, and that the format gives a clear indication of who is speaking at any one time. Advise the children that characters may interrupt each other, but that two people rarely (if ever – at this level at least) talk at the same time during a scripted performance – the lines will nearly always be spoken in sequence.

Ensure that the children understand that, contrary to other written speech, scripts do not contain speech marks or quotation marks because the whole text is known and understood to be speech and so they are unnecessary.

Follow this exercise by reading and discussing an extract from any playscript, exploring how the text indicates who is speaking, analysing the sequencing of the speech and reaffirming the concept of characters speaking in turn.

As a final note, when reading the playscript in this book, ask the children to suggest what the purpose of the words in brackets or italics might be. They may reply: 'How characters say things', 'What characters do' and 'How characters do things'. Keep the language as simple as this initially, developing the children's vocabulary gradually as they become familiar with reading and understanding scripts. (See 'Literacy support' on page 48.)

THEMES AND ISSUES IN THE PLAY

At its very simplest level, *The Clown Who Couldn't Smile* explores the problems facing the central character's emotional dilemma and its resulting implications. However, the play also provides teachers with the opportunity to examine and discuss the concept of 'happiness' and what makes us feel happy.

This can promote work which forms links with a number of PSHE issues, such as 'families' and 'friendships', and should encourage discussions about whether the state of happiness arises from materialistic gain or through other means.

Young children will also appreciate the physical aspects of this play, and its contents provide many opportunities to include a variety of movement or dance routines, from simple clowning or slapstick through to a complete circus show. Ideal for providing material for dance or PE lessons!

Music lessons can also be used to select suitable musical extracts for the play, with the children suggesting appropriate music to accompany the play itself and the various circus routines within it.

As a basic playscript, *The Clown Who Couldn't Smile* is an upbeat, moralistic and gentle play which poses no threat to its young actors and resolves its dilemma without trauma; but the contents and context of the play can provide stimuli for a variety of other creative subjects, and as a platform to develop the children's self-awareness.

WORKSHOP SESSIONS

These sessions should take place prior to any rehearsals or practical application of the playscript. They introduce the children to drama and theatre, develop their speaking and listening skills, generate positive group interaction, increase their levels of concentration, help to prepare them for the types of activity they will be doing during work on the playscript, and develop their ability to perform confidently and effectively.

SESSION 1
INTRODUCTORY WARM-UP

Timing: Spend up to 15 minutes on each individual activity. The whole session should take no more than 45 minutes.

Resources: A large space (such as the school hall), whistle, chairs (optional).

Objectives: To introduce the children to the concept of drama, promote positive group interaction and encourage the children to respond appropriately to instructions.

PIP, SQUEAK, WILFRED
A PHYSICAL WARM-UP

Ask the children to sit in a circle on the floor or on chairs. Go around the circle, naming each child Pip, Squeak or Wilfred in sequence. Explain that when you call out one of these names, all the children with that name should run in a clockwise direction around the outside of the circle. Inform the children that they must continue to run around the outside of the circle until you call out the instruction 'Home'. Upon this command, the children should continue running in the same direction back to their original places and sit down.

This makes the game a race to get 'home' first. The last child to sit down loses a life. Explain that each child has two (or three) lives to lose (adapt the number according to the size of your group). If children lose all of their lives, they are 'out' and should either turn

their chair around or quietly leave the circle. Two or three names can be called in unison.

Tell the children not to push any other group members and remind them to always run in a clockwise direction, continuing to run until given the command 'Home'. Give each name at least two turns. Ask any children who are 'out' to join the circle again, and move on to…

PASS THE MIME
INTRODUCES PERFORMANCE SKILLS AND PROMOTES CALM

Sit in the circle with the children. Inform them that you are going to make a facial expression and that they must all 'pass on' this face around the circle and back to you. Advise them that the facial expression must remain the same all the way around. Begin by passing around a happy, smiling face. Continue by passing on a frown, an angry face, an excited face, a sad face and finally, a happy face again.

Each face can be given to any child to pass on, so long as it continues right around the circle. Finally, pass on two facial expressions at the same time: a sad face in one direction and a happy face in the other. Repeat the process as many times as necessary until you and the children are satisfied that they have all passed on each type of face at least once.

If chairs have been used, ask the childern to put them away, and then to form teams of up to six, before moving on to…

MOVEMENT RELAY

DEVELOPS CO-OPERATION AND INTRODUCES MOVEMENT SKILLS

Instruct each team to form a line facing the other end of the room. Tell the children that they are going to run a relay race. Teams should be of equal numbers (if any have fewer participants some team members will need to race more than once). Explain that each team member must travel to the other end of the room and back again using a different method of movement. For example, if the first team member runs, the second must walk, and so on. Other methods could include walking backwards, hopping, crawling, skipping, and so on.

Allow each team up to 2 minutes to discuss and agree the different methods of movement they will each use. Specify the place you wish the children to run to and explain that the next team member cannot move until the previous one returns and touches them.

Ensure that all teams are lined up fairly, with no children starting ahead of others. Tell the children that the winning team will be those children who have all moved in different ways, returned to their team's starting position and who are all sitting cross-legged on the floor.

Ensure that all of the children understand the rules and then blow your whistle for the relay race to start. Watch carefully for any children not abiding by the rules. They should return to the beginning and start again. Encourage children to cheer their team mates on as they race. After the race is completed, praise all of the children for their innovative methods of movement. Congratulate the winning team, then ask the children to sit in a circle again, and end with...

CIRCLE

CHILDREN REFLECT ON AND EVALUATE THEIR SKILLS

Ask the children whether or not they enjoyed the drama session. Ask for opinions and reasons. What do they think they have learned and achieved from it?

This feedback gives an indication of any skills and knowledge gained and can be used as a basis for developing and evaluating the children's abilities during additional workshop sessions.

SESSION 2
APPROACHING THE TEXT

Timing: Spend up to 15 minutes on each activity. The whole session should take no more than 60 minutes.

Resources: Copies of the script (one per child); script extracts and groupings prepared for small-group reading, board or flip chart, sheet of A3 paper, marker pen.

Objective: To familiarize children with the play text.

SHARED TEXT WORK
WHOLE-CLASS READING OF THE SCRIPT

Sit with the children in a circle, or with them in their classroom places and hand out a copy of the playscript to each child. If applicable, remind the children of the drama exercise they experienced on understanding scripts (see 'Guidance for working with scripts' on page 5).

Tell the children that now you are all going to read a play called *The Clown Who Couldn't Smile*. Inform them that you will read the lines spoken by all of the characters at first, but that later you will invite some of them to read some of the lines spoken by the characters. Ask the children to read and follow the words in the script while you are reading. (Read the lines only; do not mention who is speaking or read out stage directions).

A suggested read-through of the play is as follows:

1. After reading approximately one third of the script yourself, ask for volunteers to contribute by reading aloud two or three lines spoken by some of the characters. A good occasion for this is during Scene 5. Ask for only one or two children to volunteer to read the lines spoken by CLOWN 1, CLOWN 2 and/or CLOWN 4. Continue to read the additional lines yourself.

2. Read the script together for only a short while, stopping at the stage direction '*The CLOWNS all start the chase sequences*'. Thank the children for their efforts.

3. Continue to read the script yourself and then repeat the exercise of asking volunteers to read one or two lines aloud with you. This should occur during Scene 6 after '*There is a long pause whilst they all try to think of a solution*'.

4. Nominate children to read the subsequent lines spoken by either SAM, GEMMA, PHILLIP and/or CARL. Again, read the additional lines yourself.

5. As before, read the script together for only a short while, stopping when BEN says 'Right! Let's go'. Thank the children for their efforts.

6. Read the remainder of the script yourself whilst the children continue to follow the text until the play reading has been completed. Ask the children to turn back to the first page of the script, and move quickly on to…

FOCUSED WORD WORK
EXPLORING THE LANGUAGE USED IN THE PLAYSCRIPT

Invite the children to suggest words from the text which they have difficulty in understanding. Specify that these must be words that they have never seen or heard before. Write these words on the board, working through the script quickly and recording as many suggestions as possible from the children.

Use any remaining time to provide definitions of the words. This can be achieved in a number of different ways:

- Children looking up the words in a dictionary, working individually with teacher guidance.
- Children working in pairs or small groups, being allocated three or four words per pair or group, and looking them up in a dictionary.
- The teacher providing definitions of the words on the board.
- The teacher providing definitions of some of the words on the board, but asking the children to discover the definitions of others.
- The teacher encouraging the children to define words from their context in the playscript.

The process of defining words can be made more interesting by creating teams and allocating a 'team point' each time a word is defined correctly. Ensure that the children record the words and their definitions – on paper, in spelling books, or in writing books. Leave any words not defined for further work at a later time, and move on to…

GROUP WORK
SMALL-GROUP READING OF THE PLAYSCRIPT

Arrange the children into groups of six to eight. (It is best if these are of mixed reading ability.) Ensure that each child has a copy of the playscript. Tell them that you are going to ask each group to read out a scene from the play, with different group members speaking the lines of different characters. Allocate each group a different extract of the play to read together.

The script could be divided into five shorter sections as follows:

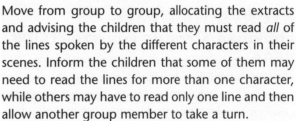

- From the beginning of Scene 2 to 'FLIPPY: Yeah, pull yourself together, Bonzo!…'
- From 'LUCINDA: I'm telling you, Raymond…' to 'ACROBAT 4: Come on then, let's go!'
- From the beginning of Scene 5 to 'CHARLE CHUCKLE: No problem, we'll soon have that sorted out…'
- From 'SAM: So you've tried painting a smile on?' to 'BEN: Right! Let's go.'
- From the beginning of Scene 7 to 'BONZO: Right! Let's get to work.'

Move from group to group, allocating the extracts and advising the children that they must read *all* of the lines spoken by the different characters in their scenes. Inform the children that some of them may need to read the lines for more than one character, while others may have to read only one line and then allow another group member to take a turn.

Move around the groups again, ensuring that roles and lines have been fairly distributed amongst the children. When you are satisfied that this preparation is completed, ask the children to begin their readings in their small groups. Move around the room, monitoring the readings and assisting where necessary. Allow sufficient time for all readings to be completed. If sufficient time remains, ask the groups in sequence to read their scenes aloud to the rest of the class.

Thank the children for their efforts. Ask them to stop reading, tell them to turn and face the board again and move on to…

STORY OUTLINE
WHOLE-CLASS REVIEW AND CONSOLIDATION OF KNOWLEDGE GAINED

Attach the sheet of A3 paper to the board. Write the heading 'The Clown Who Couldn't Smile' on it. Invite the children to recall the story told in the playscript, asking them to suggest sentences that provide a sequential outline of the events. Prompt their observations by asking: *What is the first important thing that happens in the play?* Record their answer on the A3 paper.

Follow this by asking: *And what is the next most important thing that happens?* Continue in this fashion until you have the complete story of the events of the play written on the A3 paper in sequential outline form.

Take a final moment to confirm with the children that you have recorded all of the events of the play. Thank the children for their contributions and retain the story outline for use in the following session.

SESSION 3
EXPLORING THE STORYLINE

Timing: Spend up to 20 minutes on each activity. The whole session should take no more than 60 minutes.

Resources: A large space (such as the school hall), the A3 story outline sheet from the previous session, an object to use as the 'magic microphone'.

Objectives: To consolidate knowledge of the play contents and develop drama skills.

STORYLINE MIMES
PROVIDES A FOCUS FOR STORYLINE RECALL

Sit with the children in a circle. Keep the A3 sheet of paper from the previous session close by. Invite the children to recall the story outline of the play that they created at the end of the previous session. Bring forward the A3 paper to confirm their recollections. Tell them that they are now going to perform mimes that tell the story. Inform the children that miming is moving without any sound.

Advise the children that their mimes will include:

● BONZO getting the clown act wrong
● BONZO being very unhappy and people trying to cheer him up
● BONZO at the clown school
● BONZO and TANYA having fun.

Form the children into small groups, of up to eight, and ask each group to stand in a space. Tell the children that the first mime you want them to perform is of Bonzo getting the clown act wrong.

Advise the children to negotiate distribution of characters fairly and to express their characters clearly using their faces and bodies. Instruct them to show what happens in their scene or story section by using movement only. Ensure that all of the children are clear about what is expected of them and allow each group up to 1 minute to prepare their mimes.

When the time limit has elapsed, ask all of the groups to perform their mimes in unison. Praise the children for their efforts, commenting positively on any effective performances. Some mimes may take longer than others; those groups finishing sooner should be asked to sit down quietly and watch the other performances. When all of the groups have completed their mimes, allocate each group another scene or section of the story from the story outline or from the above list.

Allow a minute for the children to prepare their mimes in their groups. Then ask all of the groups to perform their mimes in unison. Repeat this process until the children have performed short mimes representing up to five aspects of the story. Thank the children for their efforts, praise their work and move quickly on to...

MAGIC MICROPHONE
DEVELOPS LISTENING SKILLS AND STORYLINE SEQUENCING

Bring forward your object to be used as the 'magic microphone'. Sit with the children in a circle.

Inform the children that they are all going to tell the story of what happens in *The Clown Who Couldn't Smile*. Advise them that they will take turns to speak into the magic microphone and tell different parts of the story. Explain that the magic microphone will be passed around the circle and each person in turn will tell the next bit of the story. Ask for a volunteer to begin telling the story of what happens in the play. Hand this child the magic microphone and ask them to begin. After approximately 30 seconds – or when they 'run out of steam', whichever is soonest! – instruct this child to pass the magic microphone onto the person on their left for them to continue the story.

You should judge the appropriate moment for the microphone to be passed on: allow sufficient time for each child to contribute, but not too much that any child dominates the proceedings and tells all of the story. Some children will only contribute two or three words to the storytelling and this is perfectly acceptable. Continue to encourage the children to pass the magic microphone around the circle until the entire story has been told. Thank the children for their efforts, praise their work and move quickly on to...

STORYLINE FREEZES
PROVIDES A FOCUS FOR HIGHLIGHTING ELEMENTS OF THE STORY

Sit with the children in a circle. Keep the A3 paper from the previous session close by. Invite the children to recall the story outline of the play that they created at the end of the previous session. Show them the A3 paper to confirm their recollections. Tell them that they are now going to make different 'freezes' (still and silent pictures) which tell the story. Advise the children that these will include:

● BONZO getting the clown act wrong
● MR BIG telling BONZO to go to clown school
● BONZO making everyone at the clown school unhappy

- BONZO sitting sadly alone after being asked to leave the clown school
- BONZO meeting the children
- BONZO and TANYA practising the clown act together
- BONZO finally being happy and smiling.

Inform the children that you will ask them either to work alone, in pairs or in small groups to make their freezes, and that all of the freezes will be performed in unison. Ask the children to form groups of up to eight (or as near to eight as possible, according to class numbers), and to find a space to work in. Advise them that they are to listen carefully for your command to 'Freeze!' and that, on hearing this, they should stand still and silently in their positions.

Tell the children that you want them to work in their groups to create a freeze of BONZO getting the clown act wrong. Allow the children up to 20 seconds to create their freezes. After this time has elapsed, give a countdown of 3, 2, 1 and, on the count of 1, command the children to 'freeze'. Ask the children to hold these positions for a few seconds, viewing and praising each freeze yourself, then ask the children to find a partner and stand in a space.

Instruct them to make a freeze of MR BIG telling BONZO to go to the clown school. Count down from 3 again, give the 'Freeze!' command and ask them to hold the positions for a few seconds again. View and praise the freezes and then ask the children to form groups of up to seven people (or as near as possible, according to class numbers).

Tell the children to make a freeze which shows BONZO making everyone unhappy at the clown school. Allow up to 20 seconds preparation time. Count down from 3 again and give the 'Freeze!' command. Ask the children to hold the positions again, and view and praise their freezes. Then ask the children to stand in a space alone. Instruct them to freeze individually in the position of BONZO sitting sadly alone after being asked to leave the clown school. Count down from 3, give the 'Freeze!' command and hold, view and praise the freezes again.

Ask the children to form groups of up to 6 people (or as near as possible). Tell them to make a freeze that shows BONZO meeting the children. Allow extra preparation time again before giving the countdown and 'Freeze!' command, and hold, view and praise again.

Ask the children to find a partner and a space to work in. Instruct them to make a freeze that shows BONZO and TANYA practising the clown act. Count down from 3, give the 'Freeze!' command. Hold, view and praise the freezes again.

Lastly, ask the children to stand alone in a space.

Tell them that you want them all to freeze individually in the position of BONZO finally being happy and smiling. Give the count down and 'Freeze!' command, and hold, view and praise these final freezes.

Tell the children to relax, thank them for their efforts and ask them to sit in a circle with you again.

CIRCLE
CHILDREN REFLECT ON AND EVALUATE THEIR SKILLS AND KNOWLEDGE

Ask the children if they enjoyed the drama session. Invite opinions and reasons.

- What do they think they have learned and achieved from it?
- What do they feel they have done well? What could they have done better?
- How do they think the activities could help them when they are performing?
- What have they learned about the story of *The Clown Who Couldn't Smile*?

This information could be used as a basis for future workshop sessions.

SESSION 4
CHARACTERIZATION AND ROLE-PLAY

Timing: Spend up to 15 minutes on each activity. The whole session should take no more than 60 minutes.

Resources: A large space (such as the school hall), whistle, chairs (optional).

Objectives: To explore the characters in the play and encourage appropriate use of movement and language for role-play.

EMOTION FREEZES
INTRODUCES THE CONCEPT OF EXPRESSION

Ask the children to walk around the room carefully, without bumping or touching each other. Advise them to listen out for your whistle. After a short time, blow the whistle, call out a specific emotion, mood or feeling, (such as 'Happy!'), and tell the children to freeze instantly in the position of someone feeling or expressing that particular emotion. (Or sad, angry, lonely, excited – the choice is yours, so long as all the children freeze expressing the same emotion.) Remind the children that the 'Freeze' command instructs them to be completely still and silent.

Advise them that their freezes can be realistic (someone experiencing that emotion in a particular setting), or abstract (showing how that emotion feels by creating an unusual shape with their bodies).

After each freeze, ask the children to hold their positions for a few seconds. Move around the room, viewing each freeze and commenting positively on them, praising in particular those children whose freezes are imaginative or expressive, or who are 'freezing' effectively. Tell the children to relax and to continue walking around the room as before.

Repeat the exercise, blowing the whistle and calling out a different emotion, mood or feeling. Remember to praise effective freezes each time. Repeat until the children have created at least five freezes and then move on to…

WALKABOUT IN ROLE
DEVELOPS CHARACTER MOVEMENT

Ask the children to walk around the room carefully again. Tell them that this time they are to listen carefully for you calling out the name of one of the characters from the play. Stress that it is essential that they walk in silence in order to hear your commands. Explain that, when they hear you call the character name they are to continue walking around the room, but in the style and manner of that character. Tell the children that, after walking as the character for a while, you will then instruct them to 'walk as themselves again'.

Call out a character name from the play, such as BONZO, and instruct the children to 'Walk about as…' (Again, the choice of character is yours, but all should walk about as the same character).

Watch the children as they walk about in role, commenting positively on those children expressing the character well in their movements. After a short while instruct the children to 'Walk as yourselves again.' Then repeat the 'Walk about' instruction using a different character from the play.

Continue until the children have walked around the room in the manner of at least four different characters from the play. Then ask the children to stop walking and thank them for their efforts. Ask them to find a partner and a space to work in, and move quickly on to…

CLOWN FACES
BUILDS SUBJECT-SPECIFIC CREATIVE SKILLS

Ask the children to sit facing their partners. Advise them that you want them to mime making up their partner's face with imaginary make-up to create a happy, smiling clown face. Tell the children that they should be very specific in their use of colours and that they must describe the application in fine detail to their partners during the process of creating the make-up effect.

Ask the children to label themselves 'A' or 'B'. (For groups with an odd number, a 'C' can be added to one pair, or the teacher can work with the child). Instruct the children that As will apply the clown make-up to Bs first. (Pairs with a C should take alternate turns to make each other up). Remind the children that they must tell their partners what colours and shapes they are using to decorate their faces and that they should take time and care over the process. Ensure that all of the children understand your instructions and then ask them to begin making up their partners. Move around the room to assess the children's efforts, praising any who are concentrating well.

Allow up to 2 minutes for the As to apply the clown make-up to the Bs. Instruct the children to swap roles, so that the Bs apply clown make-up to the As. Again, ensure that all of the children are performing the task properly and praise effective efforts. Allow up to 2 minutes for this make-up mime to continue.

Now ask the children to repeat the process, but this time creating a sad clown face instead of a happy one. Advise them to consider the different shapes they might paint and the difference this might make to their choice of colours. Instruct Bs to begin by applying the sad clown make-up to their As. Allow this to continue for up to 1 minute. Tell the children to swap roles and repeat the exercise. Remember to praise any concentrated work.

Finally, if any time is remaining, invite the children to talk about the colours and patterns they used to make-up their partners. Thank all of the children for their efforts, praise their concentration, ask them to find a new partner and a space to work in, and move quickly on to…

PAIR CONVERSATIONS
CONSOLIDATES VERBAL CHARACTERIZATION SKILLS

In their pairs, ask the children to label themselves 'A' and 'B'. (Classes with an odd number of children can include one group with a 'C'.) Advise the children that they are going to act out different characters in the play discussing BONZO and his problem. Tell the children that they are to imagine that A and B (and C if applicable) are clowns in the circus act having a conversation about the difficulty BONZO has in smiling and the effect this is having on the clown act.

Instruct the children to act out this conversation without any planning or preparation. Allow the conversations to continue in unison for up to 30 seconds whilst you move around the room, praising those children who are expressing the characters well and enacting the situation effectively.

After this time has elapsed, change the situation so that A now becomes LUCINDA, B becomes RAYMOND (and if applicable, C becomes the STRONG MAN). Tell the children to enact these characters discussing BONZO and his problems. Again, no planning or preparation time should be allocated and the conversations should be allowed to continue for up to 30 seconds. Move around the room, listening to each conversation and praising where applicable.

In a third situation, tell them to imagine that they are the children discussing BONZO and his problem. Again, allow these conversations to continue for up to 30 seconds and praise as appropriate.

Finally, instruct the children that A is now BONZO'S MUM and B is AUNTY VAL (if applicable, C is cousin TANYA) and tell them to act out a conversation between these characters where they discuss BONZO and his problems.

Explain to the children that each set of characters will have a different reaction to BONZO's problems and that they should consider this carefully when improvising. This should discourage the children from simply repeating lines.

When the children have enacted each situation, praise their work, thank them for their efforts, ask them to sit in a circle with you and end with...

CIRCLE
CHILDREN REFECT ON AND EVALUATE THEIR SKILLS AND KNOWLEDGE

Ask the children whether or not they enjoyed the drama session. Invite opinions and reasons.

- What do they think they have learned and achieved from it?
- What do they feel they have done well?
- What do they feel they could have done better?
- How do they think the activities could help them when they are performing?
- What have they learned about the characters in *The Clown Who Couldn't Smile*?

This information could be used as a basis for future workshop sessions.

SESSION 5
CONSOLIDATING PERFORMANCE SKILLS

Timing: Spend up to 20 minutes on each activity. The whole session should take no more than 60 minutes.

Resources: A large space (such as the school hall), copies of the playscript, chairs (optional), A3 paper and pen (optional).

Objectives: To consolidate knowledge of the play and provide a focus for performance skills.

EXPRESSIVE ACTIONS
DEVELOPS MOVEMENT SKILLS

Ask the children to form pairs and to stand in a space facing their partner. Tell them that you are going to ask them to react to each other in mime that you want these mimed reactions to be very 'big', with lots of energy and large movements. Remind the children that mime is movement without sound or words.

Ask the children to work with their partner and mime being very pleased to see them, as if they haven't met for some time. Suggest that their movements could include giving and receiving big hugs, shaking hands vigorously, patting each other enthusiastically on the shoulders, and so on. Remind the children that these movements must be large, 'over the top' and very energetic, but stress that they must also take care not to hurt their partners. The reactions should be spontaneous, with no planning or preparation time allowed. Praise any pairs reacting effectively.

When each pair has reacted in this manner, instruct the children to react next as if they are both very shocked. Again, these reactions should be mimed and should be expressed using 'big' facial and body movements.

Then ask the children to mime laughing at each other, as if their partner has done something very silly or stupid. Remind them that their movements must include no sound and must be large and expressive. Praise effective mimes.

Finally, ask the children to react as if they are extremely angry with their partner. Advise them that no physical contact is permitted. Actions could include shaking fists at each other, folding arms and turning away, and so on. Praise effective mimes.

When each pair has mimed their reactions, thank all of the children for their efforts and ask them to sit in a circle with you. Invite the children to suggest possible links between this activity and the play. Answers should focus on their mimed reactions being similar to those found in clown performances at the circus. Praise all contributions, thank the children for their suggestions and move on to…

HAPPINESS IS…
DEVELOPS UNDERSTANDING OF THE PLAY CONTEXT

Remain sitting in a circle and ask the children: *Why can't BONZO smile?* Their responses should include 'because he is unhappy'. Ask the children to suggest why Bonzo is unhappy and, then, to consider what makes him happy and able to smile again. Respond positively to all suggestions and contributions.

Continue the discussion by asking: *What makes you happy?* Allow the group discussion to continue for up to 5 minutes. Acknowledge all responses and thank the children for their comments then ask them to form groups of up to six people (or as near to six as possible, according to class numbers).

Inform the children that you want them to work in their groups to create a freeze of an activity or situation that makes them happy. Point out that this can be one of the suggestions heard during the discussion, or another of their own devising. Instruct the children that you will allow a short time for planning and preparation, and then will view each of the 'happiness' freezes in turn.

Ensure that all of the children understand what is expected of them and allow up to 2 minutes for their planning and preparation. Move quickly from group to group, ensuring that children are not spending too much time on discussion. When the time limit has elapsed, and each group has prepared their freezes, view each freeze in turn. Insist that the audience remains silent whilst each group shows their freeze and then invite the observers to suggest what each freeze depicts. Encourage the audience to applaud after each freeze. When all of the freezes have been seen, thank and praise the children for their efforts, ask them to sit down, and move quickly on to…

SCRIPT EXTRACTS
REINTRODUCES THE SCRIPT AND PREPARES CHILDREN FOR PERFORMANCE

Tell the children that you are going to ask them to act out parts of the script aloud to each other. Advise them that their performances can either simply be read aloud, or can be acted out with movements as well. Distribute copies of the script, retaining one for yourself. Form the children into groups and allocate script extracts for performance. You could use the following extracts or make your own selections (these extracts can be reduced or expanded to suit class size).

- Six to eight children: from the beginning of Scene 2 to just before the Acrobats' entrance.
- Six to seven children: Scene 3.
- Six to seven children: Scene 5.
- Six to seven children: Scene 6.
- Four children: Scene 7.

Advise the children that some of them may have to read or act the lines for more than one character if there are fewer people in their group than character parts in their extract. The aim is to enable the children to learn how to read, prepare and perform the script. Performances can be static or moved, but encourage the children to use vocal and facial expression.

Allow children up to 5 minutes to read and practise their script extracts. Ask each group to read or show their pieces in sequence – according to events in the play. Invite those observing as audience members to applaud the other groups after each performance. When each group has performed their script extract, thank the children for their work, praise their efforts, ask them to sit in a circle again, and end with…

CIRCLE
CHILDREN REFLECT ON AND EVALUATE THEIR SKILLS AND KNOWLEDGE

Ask the children if they enjoyed the drama session. Invite opinions and reasons.

- Which aspects did they enjoy the most and the least?
- What do they think they have learned or achieved from the session?
- What do they feel is the most important skill they have learned?
- What do they feel they have done well? What could they have done better?
- How do they feel about their performances?
- What would they change/do better if they had the chance to perform again?
- What do they feel is the most important thing to remember when performing in front of an audience?

Acknowledge all responses, thank the children for their hard work and praise their efforts. You may wish to record their answers on the A3 paper to provide a visual prompt during rehearsals of the play.

The Clown who couldn't Smile

CAST LIST

Ringmaster	**Clown 1 – Groucho**
Cheeko the clown	**Clown 2 – Max**
Flippy the clown	**Clown 3 – Monty**
Bonzo the clown	**Clown 4 – Harpo**
Pipo the clown	**Clown 5 – Freddy**
Dippy the clown	**Phillip**
Toppo the clown	**Carl**
Whizzo the clown	**Ben**
Gingo the clown	**Gemma**
The Strong Man – 'The Great Suprendo'	**Samantha**
	Louise
Acrobat 1 – Karloff	**Mrs Smith** (*Bonzo's mum*)
Acrobat 2 – Turnoff	
Acrobat 3 – Checkoff	**Aunty Val** (*Bonzo's aunty*)
Acrobat 4 – Topoff	
Lucinda (*trapeze artist*)	**Cousin Tanya** (*Bonzo's cousin and Aunty Val's daughter*)
Raymond (*trapeze artist*)	
Mr Big (*owner of the circus*)	
Charlie Chuckle (*head of the clown school*)	**32 characters**

SCENES

1 The 'Big Top' circus arena
2 After the show
3 At the circus
4 Outside the stables
5 At the clown school
6 On a nearby hilltop
7 A short time later

CHARACTER OUTLINES

RINGMASTER: A confident character who introduces the circus acts, and the play.

CHEEKO: A kindly clown to whom the circus act is really important.

FLIPPY: A nasty clown with little consideration for others.

BONZO: A sad clown who is a kindly person made unhappy by his inability to smile.

PIPO: An unfriendly clown who can be quite sarcastic.

DIPPY: An unpleasant clown who always joins in with others and can be quite nasty.

TOPPO: A nice clown who worries about the problems of others.

WHIZZO: A friendly clown with a sympathetic nature.

GINGO: A jolly clown who cares a great deal about the circus audiences.

STRONG MAN: A kindly man who tries to help but sometimes says the wrong thing.

ACROBAT 1: A jolly, happy person who always tries to look on the bright side of problems.

ACROBAT 2: A cheerful person who tries to make others feel happier.

ACROBAT 3: A posh person who is friendly and kind.

ACROBAT 4: A slightly dim but friendly person who agrees with everyone.

LUCINDA: Can be quite sarcastic and nasty, but concerned about Bonzo.

RAYMOND: Kind towards Bonzo but can be unpleasant when irritated by others – especially Lucinda.

MR BIG: A self-important man with a lot of power. He's usually fair but very firm.

CHARLIE CHUCKLE: An experienced, older clown who is irritated by silly people.

CLOWN 1: A stupid clown who often says or does the wrong thing.

CLOWN 2: A show-off and a bit of a big-head.

CLOWN 3: A clown with a slightly nasty temper who can be unpleasant.

CLOWN 4: A sarcastic clown who can be very nasty to others.

CLOWN 5: A miserable clown who is easily affected by the behaviour of others.

PHILLIP: A confident person, but he often says the wrong thing.

CARL: Can be quite sarcastic. Asks a lot of questions and occasionally states the obvious.

BEN: Quite nasty to others. Has little sympathy for Bonzo. Aggressive and gets bored easily.

GEMMA: Kind natured and very supportive of Bonzo.

SAMANTHA: Intelligent and kind. Tries very hard to find a solution to Bonzo's problem.

LOUISE: Has a sympathetic nature and tries to stop others from being unkind.

MRS SMITH: Jolly and loud-voiced. Always trying to get Bonzo to do favours for her.

AUNTY VAL: A good-natured person who tries not to upset others.

COUSIN TANYA: A happy person with a positive outlook on life who is kind towards Bonzo.

Photocopiable

SCENE 1: **The 'Big Top' circus arena**

The RINGMASTER enters and stands in front of the closed curtains. He speaks over the music. Circus music is played quietly throughout the following speech.

RINGMASTER: Ladies, gentlemen and children! Welcome to the Big Top Circus. We have an extravaganza of entertainment for you tonight! There are tightrope walkers, trapeze artists, the world's strongest man, acrobats, magicians, bareback riders and lots, lots more. But first, to introduce our thrilling show, we have those masters of merriment – the Big Top clowns!

The RINGMASTER exits and the curtains open quickly.
The circus music increases in volume. The CLOWNS enter immediately to perform their circus act. As the CLOWNS perform their circus act, one CLOWN (BONZO) gets everything wrong. The CLOWNS continue to try and finish their act as best they can. The music ends, the CLOWNS all bow and the lights fade to blackout.
The CLOWNS all exit.

SCENE 2: **After the performance**

The CLOWNS are all changing after the show. They are getting ready to leave.

CHEEKO: *(to BONZO)* What happened to you tonight, Bonzo? You weren't funny at all!

BONZO: Sorry.

FLIPPY: Sorry?! You made a real mess of the act.

BONZO: *(sadly)* I know.

PIPO: You were about as funny as an *EastEnders* omnibus!

TOPPO: *(to BONZO)* What's wrong?

BONZO: I don't know, I just don't want to be funny anymore.

Photocopiable

DIPPY: You're telling me! I've seen funnier party political broadcasts!

CHEEKO: All right, Dippy, don't keep having a go at him. *(To Bonzo)* Has something happened to upset you?

BONZO: No, not really.

GINGO: Then what is it? We're clowns – we're supposed to make people laugh!

WHIZZO: *(to BONZO)* Have you had some bad news? Are you feeling ill?

BONZO: No, no, nothing like that.

TOPPO: Then what is it?

BONZO: I don't know, I just feel all sad inside and when I tried to paint my face on, I couldn't get it to go into a smile, all I could manage was this sad mouth.

GINGO: Blimey! It's enough to make you weep. Whoever heard of a miserable clown?!

DIPPY: Well, you'd better snap out of it!

FLIPPY: Yeah, pull yourself together, Bonzo! We don't want another night like tonight.

The CLOWNS all exit, leaving BONZO alone. He sits on his own, sighing sadly. The STRONG MAN, LUCINDA and RAYMOND enter.

STRONG MAN: Lucinda and Raymond and I are going for a McDonald's, do you want to come with us?

BONZO: No thanks, Strong Man.

LUCINDA: What's wrong, Bonzo? You seem a little down in the mouth.

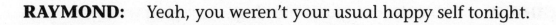

RAYMOND: Yeah, you weren't your usual happy self tonight.

BONZO: I just don't seem to be able to smile at the moment. I couldn't even smile at your trapeze act, and I usually love that.

STRONG MAN: Well I don't want to make you feel worse, but I think the Ringmaster's really upset about the clown act not going well. He was looking for you earlier, sorry.

LUCINDA: Oh, what did you go and tell him that for? He's already feeling miserable.

STRONG MAN: I just thought he ought to be prepared, that's all.

RAYMOND: Do you want us to stay with you, Bonzo, in case the Ringmaster turns up?

BONZO: No, that's all right. You go off and enjoy yourselves.

RAYMOND: Well, if you're sure? *(BONZO nods)* Bye, then, we'll see you later.

LUCINDA: Hope you're feeling better soon.

The STRONG MAN, LUCINDA and RAYMOND exit.
BONZO is left alone again.

BONZO: *(unhappily to himself)* Oh, great! That's all I need, the Ringmaster after me! Well, there's nothing I can do about it. I can't smile and that's that!

The four ACROBATS enter.

ACROBAT 1: Hey Bonzo! You're talking to yourself!

ACROBAT 2: Yeah! First sign of madness, you know!

BONZO: *(jumping nervously)* Oh! Hello, acrobats, I didn't hear you come in.

ACROBAT 3: You look a bit glum, old chap. Anything wrong?

BONZO: Well, no, not unless you count the fact that I can't smile and the Ringmaster's after me because I got everything wrong tonight.

ACROBAT 4: You can't smile?

BONZO: No.

ACROBAT 1: Well, why didn't you paint a smile on?

BONZO: I tried to, but I just felt so unhappy that I couldn't.

ACROBAT 2: That's bad news. Especially for a clown.

ACROBAT 3: Yeah. You need something to make you feel happy.

ACROBAT 4: Did you watch any of the show? That usually makes us smile.

BONZO: I watched all of it. It always made me happy before, but tonight nothing made any difference.

ACROBAT 1: Not even us?

BONZO: Not the trapeze artists, or the strong man or the bareback riders, or even you with your wonderful acrobatic routine. None of it made any difference.

ACROBAT 3: Dear, dear, dear. You are in a bad way, aren't you?

BONZO: I just wish I knew where my smile had gone. I could get it back then.

There is a pause whilst they all think about this.

ACROBAT 2: *(excitedly)* Why don't you get one of the other clowns to paint a smile on for you?

ACROBAT 4: Yes! That should work.

Photocopiable

ACROBAT 1: And, once the smile is painted on, you should feel happier and be your old self again.

BONZO: It's worth a try. I'll get one of the others to do it for me tomorrow night. Thanks!

ACROBAT 2: You're welcome.

ACROBAT 3: Just hope it works, old bean, that's all.

ACROBAT 4: Well, painting a smile on your face must get you half-way to feeling happy, mustn't it?

ACROBAT 1: I would think so. It seems to work for other people, anyway.

ACROBAT 2: We ought to be going now, you lot. We've got that new routine to practice.

ACROBAT 3: Goodness me! I clean forgot. Yes, we'll have to dash now, Bonzo.

ACROBAT 4: Keep... *(stops suddenly)* ...I nearly said 'keep smiling'! Keep your chin up.

ACROBAT 1: Yeah, try not to let it get you down. See you tomorrow!

BONZO: Bye, and thanks.

The ACROBATS all exit. BONZO is left alone again.

BONZO: *(sadly)* Keep smiling! I wish I could smile. I don't know what's happened to me. Yesterday I was a clown with a big smiley face and suddenly I can't seem to manage even a tiny grin.

Suddenly the RINGMASTER rushes in.

BONZO: *(jumps up in fright)* Oh!

RINGMASTER: Ah, here you are, Bonzo! I'm glad I've found you, I'd like a word with you.

Photocopiable

BONZO: I know, I know. You're cross at me for messing up the act and for looking so miserable and you want me to cheer up.

RINGMASTER: *(a bit deflated)* Er, yes, that's about it. And there'd better be an improvement in the show tomorrow or you and I will be doing some serious talking!

BONZO: *(fed up)* Right, right.

RINGMASTER: The children expect clowns to be funny and silly and to mess about and be happy, with daft, smiley faces.

BONZO: I know, I know.

RINGMASTER: Well, if you know, why the sad face and the miserable behaviour? It's not what clowns do!

BONZO: I know.

RINGMASTER: So don't do it again.

BONZO: All right, all right, Ringmaster! Don't worry, everything'll be all right for tomorrow night.

RINGMASTER: Good.

The RINGMASTER exits angrily. BONZO sits alone and tries to smile, but finds he can't.

BONZO: Nope. I definitely can't smile. I only hope the other clowns can help me to get my smile back.

BONZO exits sadly.

SCENE 3: **At the circus**

A CHARACTER walks across the stage and says to the audience: Four days later. The ACROBATS enter and are practising their routine when the STRONG MAN rushes in.

STRONG MAN: Acrobats! Have you heard the news? Mr Big is on his way!

ACROBAT 2: *(surprised)* No?!

ACROBAT 3: Mr Big? You mean the Mr Big who owns this circus?

STRONG MAN: Why, do you know another Mr Big?

ACROBAT 3: Well, no, you have a point.

ACROBAT 1: What's he coming for?

STRONG MAN: Well, the news is that he's here to speak to Bonzo.

ACROBAT 4: Oh, no! I know he hasn't been doing very well, but you don't think he'll get rid of him, do you?

ACROBAT 2: Well I wouldn't be surprised. He still hasn't managed to smile, has he?

ACROBAT 4: Well, no, but he surely wouldn't get rid of him just because of that, would he?

ACROBAT 1: I don't know. I mean, whoever heard of a clown who couldn't smile?

STRONG MAN: Exactly. And Bonzo has been getting worse. People have been complaining that he makes them feel miserable too, and Mr Big doesn't like that. You know how nasty he can get.

ACROBAT 3: We'd better go and warn the others!

The ACROBATS exit quickly. The STRONG MAN exits in the opposite direction. LUCINDA and RAYMOND enter. They are arguing with each other.

LUCINDA: I'm telling you, Raymond, if you don't start using underarm deodorant, you and I are finished!

RAYMOND: I don't know what you're talking about, I've never had a problem with body odour before.

LUCINDA: (nastily) Maybe it's just that no one's ever mentioned it to you.

RAYMOND: All right, all right! I'll do something about my body odour if you start using a mouthwash.

LUCINDA: (defensively) What do you mean?! I don't have a problem with bad breath!

RAYMOND: If you say so.

LUCINDA: I do say so! And while we're on the subject of personal hygiene...

The ACROBATS suddenly enter in a rush.

ACROBAT 2: Hey, you two! Have you heard the news? Mr Big is on his way!

RAYMOND: (nervously) Mr Big?

LUCINDA: (nastily to RAYMOND) He probably wants to have a word with you about your perspiration problem.

The ACROBATS all exchange puzzled glances.

ACROBAT 4: (confused) No, he's coming to talk to Bonzo.

LUCINDA: Oh, poor Bonzo. He's been having a rotten time, hasn't he?

ACROBAT 3: He certainly has, and it's going to get worse!

ACROBAT 1: We'd better go and find him to warn him, before Mr Big finds him first.

Raymond : I saw him down by the stab[le]

Acrobat 4 : Come on then lets go.

RAYMOND: I saw him down by the stables.

ACROBAT 4: Come on then, let's go!

They ALL exit quickly.

SCENE 4: **Outside the stables**

BONZO enters.

BONZO: *(sighing sadly)* I don't know what to do. Life just isn't the same when you can't smile. I've tried everything – thinking happy thoughts, getting the other clowns to paint my smile on, reading joke books – but none of it works. Nothing has kept the smile on my face.

MR BIG enters.

MR BIG: Ah! There you are, Bonzo!

BONZO: *(jumping in fear)* Mr Big!

MR BIG: Rest easy, Bonzo. I just want to have a few words with you, that's all.

BONZO: *(relaxing a little)* Right.

MR BIG: Now, as you well know, I'm not a difficult man. In fact, I've been known to be very reasonable in my time.

BONZO: Yes, sir.

MR BIG: Please, please, call me Mr Big.

BONZO: Yes, Mr Big.

MR BIG: But this can't go on, can it?

BONZO: *(sadly)* No.

Photocopiable

MR BIG: Now, as you well know, I'm not one to make a crisis out of a drama, but I do believe in resolving problems before they get out of hand.

BONZO: And I'm the problem?

MR BIG: You certainly are, Bonzo, you certainly are.

BONZO: So what's going to happen to me?

MR BIG: Well, as you well know, I am a fair-minded man and I believe in giving people second chances.

BONZO: *(hopefully)* So you're not going to sack me, then?

MR BIG: Sack you? No, no. That was one of the options I considered, I must admit; but, no, I'm not going to sack you, Bonzo, I'm sending you back to clown school.

BONZO: *(in amazement)* Back to clown school?!

MR BIG: *(irritated)* Yes, yes! I have decided that you would benefit from a refresher course in being funny. You leave this evening. I suggest that you pop along and pack your bags. You'll be gone for a week.

BONZO: But... but...

Suddenly LUCINDA and RAYMOND enter, intending to warn BONZO. They see it is too late and try to tiptoe away again without being seen by MR BIG, but he notices them.

MR BIG: Ah! Lucinda! Raymond! I'm glad I've seen you. Raymond, could I just have a brief word with you about the delicate matter of your choice of deodorant...

LUCINDA gives RAYMOND a knowing look. LUCINDA, RAYMOND and MR BIG exit, with MR BIG saying...

MR BIG: Now, as you well know, I'm not one to pry into the personal cleaning routines of my circus acts, but...

Photocopiable

BONZO stands alone, shrugs his shoulders, sighs heavily and exits.

SCENE 5: **At the clown school**

CHARLIE CHUCKLE stands in front of CLOWNS 1, 2, 3, 4 and 5 and BONZO.

CHARLIE CHUCKLE: Welcome, clowns!

ALL of the CLOWNS except BONZO fall about laughing.

CHARLIE CHUCKLE: *(annoyed)* I haven't started yet!

ALL CLOWNS EXCEPT BONZO: Oh, sorry.

CHARLIE CHUCKLE: Welcome to the Charlie Chuckle School of Clowning. My name is Charlie Chuckle...

CLOWN 1 starts laughing again. CHARLIE CHUCKLE silences him with a nasty glare.

CLOWN 1: Sorry.

CHARLIE CHUCKLE: ...and I will be your teacher for this week. We will start off with the simple exercise of tripping up.

CLOWN 2: *(showing off)* Oh, I've done this before.

CHARLIE CHUCKLE: Then you should be very good at it. Please demonstrate for the rest of us.

CLOWN 2: *(wishing he'd kept quiet now)* Oh, right.

CLOWN 2 gets up and tries to demonstrate, but makes a mess of it.

The OTHER CLOWNS (EXCEPT BONZO) all laugh.

CLOWN 3: Call that a trip up?

CLOWN 4: He can't do it!

CLOWN 5: Aren't you supposed to fall flat on your face?

CLOWN 1: I thought it was quite good, actually.

CHARLIE CHUCKLE: All right! All right! Please sit down. Bonzo, you're an experienced clown, perhaps you'd be kind enough to demonstrate for us?

BONZO trips up perfectly but does not smile.

CHARLIE CHUCKLE: Very good! But where's the smile to show that you didn't hurt yourself?

BONZO: Sorry. I'm having a bit of trouble with smiling at the moment.

CHARLIE CHUCKLE: No problem, we'll soon have that sorted out. Now, let me see you all practise those trips, please.

All of the CLOWNS get up and start practising. They all copy BONZO and, because of this, eventually none of them is smiling.

CHARLIE CHUCKLE: Stop! Stop! None of you are smiling now? Why not?

CLOWN 3: It's him! *(pointing at BONZO)*

CLOWN 4: He's making us feel miserable!

CHARLIE CHUCKLE: All right, all right. We'll try something different. Let's work on the chases, shall we? These can be performed with or without the trip up. Off you go!

The CLOWNS all start the chase sequences. As before, they end up miserable because of BONZO.

CHARLIE CHUCKLE: Stop! What is wrong with you all? I've never seen such a lack of effort in my school!

CLOWN 5: We're sorry, Mr Chuckle, but it's difficult to be funny when one of you isn't!

CLOWN 3: He's making us depressed.

CLOWN 1: *(upset)* I think I'm going to cry soon!

CLOWN 2: Why can't he look happy?

CHARLIE CHUCKLE: That's enough! *(To BONZO)* I'm sorry, but I'm going to have to ask you to leave. I don't know what's wrong with you, but I can't have this sort of behaviour in my school!

BONZO: But Mr Big sent me here to get my smile back!

CLOWN 4: Well, it isn't here, is it? And you're making us all as miserable as you are!

CHARLIE CHUCKLE: I'm sorry, Bonzo. I do hope you find your smile, but please go.

BONZO exits sadly.

CHARLIE CHUCKLE: Right! Who's for trying the poke in the eye?

CLOWN 1:	Me! Me!
CHARLIE CHUCKLE:	Right, just come and stand out here, then...

When the lights fade to blackout, the CLOWNS and CHARLIE CHUCKLE all exit.

SCENE 6: **On a nearby hilltop**

BONZO enters sadly and sits down. PHILLIP, CARL, BEN, GEMMA, SAMANTHA and LOUISE enter.

PHILLIP:	Hey! Isn't that one of the clowns that we saw in the circus act the other night?
SAM:	Oh yes! *(Pause)* Why is he sitting here all alone?
LOUISE:	He looks so unhappy.
GEMMA:	It's not right seeing a clown miserable, is it?
CARL:	Hey! You! Mr Clown! What are you sitting here for?

BONZO jumps and stands up.

BONZO:	Oh, hello! I didn't expect anyone to be around at this time.
LOUISE:	We're on school holidays. You're from the circus, aren't you? What's your name?
BONZO:	Yes I am, I'm Bonzo.
BEN:	*(snorting with laughter)* Bonzo! What a daft name!
GEMMA:	Shut up you! It's no dafter than Ben!
CARL:	So why are you sitting up here all alone?
BEN:	*(nastily)* I bet they threw him out. I thought he was rubbish.

SAM: Oh, don't be so horrible, Ben, I thought the clowns were really good.

PHILLIP: Yes, but he wasn't as good as the others though, was he? He kept making mistakes.

LOUISE: I'm sure he doesn't need reminding, Phillip! *(To BONZO)* Is that why you're so unhappy?

BONZO: Yes. No. Well, sort of.

LOUISE: Have they thrown you out of the circus?

BONZO: No, not yet, but they will do.

SAM: Why, what's wrong?

BONZO: I can't smile.

PHILLIP: What do you mean, you can't smile? Everyone can smile.

BONZO: Well I can't. I lost my smile a couple of weeks ago and I can't get it back again.

GEMMA: *(sympathetically)* Aah. I think that's really sad.

BEN: Well, I think it's stupid. Whoever heard of a clown without a smile?

BONZO: Exactly. Nobody. That's why they'll throw me out of the circus.

CARL: But can't you just paint a smile on? That's what all the other clowns do.

BONZO: I tried that, but you need to be happy inside for that to work, and I'm not.

CARL: Is that why you kept making mistakes, then?

BONZO: *(sadly)* Yes.

Photocopiable

CARL: Well, you've got a real problem, haven't you?

BONZO: *(sadly)* I know.

LOUISE: I don't think that pointing out the obvious is going to help him, Carl.

CARL: I'm just trying to think it through, that's all; see if we can't help him to come up with a solution.

There is a long pause whilst they all try to think of a solution.

SAM: So you've tried painting a smile on?

BONZO: Yes.

SAM: And that didn't work?

BONZO: No.

GEMMA: Have you tried thinking happy thoughts? I always feel happy when I imagine a huge bowl of chocolate ice cream.

PHILLIP: And playing on my new computer makes me feel happy.

SAM: Or you could do something to cheer you up. I really like dancing to my music.

CARL: Or try watching a funny programme on television. Mr Bean always makes me laugh.

BEN: I feel really happy when I think about beating up Tommy Jackson.

LOUISE: Shut up, Ben! If you can't think of something sensible to say, don't say anything.

BEN: I was only trying to help.

GEMMA: Well you aren't, so keep quiet!

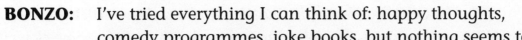

BONZO: I've tried everything I can think of: happy thoughts, comedy programmes, joke books, but nothing seems to work. Mr Big – that's the owner of the circus – even sent me back to clown school, but they threw me out because I was making all the other clowns miserable.

SAM: Oh, that's awful!

BEN: No it's not, it's boring. Let's go and find something else to do.

SAM: No! We need to think of something to help Bonzo.

BEN: Well we can't, can we? I mean, we've made lots of suggestions and he's tried them all, so that's that.

CARL: I think Ben's right, Samantha. I don't think we can suggest anything that Bonzo hasn't already tried himself.

BEN: Right! Let's go.

LOUISE: *(to BONZO)* I'm sorry, Bonzo. I don't think we can help.

GEMMA: I hope the circus don't throw you out, I think you're really nice.

PHILLIP: Yeah, you'll be really funny when you get your smile back again.

BONZO: Thank you. *(Pause)* I think.

SAM: Take care of yourself, Bonzo, and keep thinking those happy thoughts – one of them might work!

PHILLIP: *(to the others as they all exit)* Where are we going now? I vote for the park!

BEN: *(moaning)* Oh no, that's boring, we always go there!

CARL: Well you suggest something else then!

Photocopiable

The CHILDREN all exit, chatting and arguing as they go.
BONZO remains on stage alone again. He tries to perform some clowning
movements but fails and sits down sadly again.

SCENE 7: **A short time later**

A loud 'screechy' voice is heard calling offstage.

MRS SMITH: *(yelling loudly)* Bonzo!! Bonzo!! Where are you?

BONZO: *(jumping up)* Oh crickey! It's my mum! *(Shouting back)* I'm here, Mum!!

MRS SMITH enters with AUNTY VAL and COUSIN TANYA.

MRS SMITH: We've been looking all over the place for you! What are you doing moping about up here on your own? I thought you'd be at the circus practising with all the other clowns.

BONZO: *(trying to leave)* I was just on my way there.

MRS SMITH: Well, you can just stay here now! I want you to do me a favour.

BONZO: *(horrified)* Oh, not another kiddies' party for one of your friends, please!

MRS SMITH: No, no, no. Nothing like that. *(Indicating Aunty Val)* This is your Aunty Val. You remember her, don't you?

BONZO: Of course I do. *(To Aunty Val)* Hello, Aunty Val.

AUNTY VAL: Hello, Bonzo.

MRS SMITH: And this is your cousin Tanya. You probably won't recognize her; she was only young the last time you met.

TANYA: Hello, Bonzo.

BONZO: *(suspiciously to MRS SMITH)* No. *(To TANYA)* Hello.

Photocopiable

MRS SMITH: Anyway, Tanya has decided, for some unknown reason, that she wants to be a clown and I want you to show her what to do.

BONZO: *(whining)* Oh, Mum, do I have to? Now is not a really good time.

MRS SMITH: It's never a good time with you lately, is it? I really would like you to do this for me, Bonzo.

AUNTY VAL: She'll be no trouble. Personally, I'd rather she do something else, but Tanya is stubborn and when she gets an idea into her head, there's no chance of changing her mind.

BONZO: Well I'm not sure that I can help, really.

AUNTY VAL: There you go, Marjorie, I told you he'd be too busy.

BONZO: No, it's not that, I just… *(pause)* …Oh, never mind. Leave her with me, I'll see what I can do.

MRS SMITH: Thank you, Bonzo. It's very kind of you. *(To Aunty Val)* Come on, Val, let's go and have a cup of tea.

AUNTY VAL: Good idea! Now, Tanya, you behave yourself and do exactly as Bonzo tells you!

TANYA: Yes, Mum.

MRS SMITH AND AUNTY VAL: *(together)* Bye!

MRS SMITH and AUNTY VAL exit. BONZO and TANYA stand looking at each other in silence for a moment.

BONZO: Right! Let's get to work.

They begin miming some clown movements and then BOTH freeze in position. The lights go to blackout.
BONZO and TANYA move into new clown routine positions and hold them in a freeze as the lights go up again.
When the lights are fully up, TANYA trips and falls. She begins to laugh. BONZO smiles at her then laughs briefly. He stops suddenly as he realizes.

BONZO: *(amazed)* I'm smiling again!

TANYA: I know, it wasn't very good. Can I do it again?

BONZO: No, no! It isn't you! I can't believe I'm smiling again, and I laughed too! It's been such a long time since I smiled.

TANYA: Why haven't you smiled?

BONZO: I don't know. I just couldn't. Nothing made me feel happy.

TANYA: So why are you smiling now?

BONZO: *(thinking hard)* I don't know. I suppose it's because we're having fun.

TANYA: Yes, it's great doing silly things, isn't it. That's why I want to be a clown. Why did you want to be one?

BONZO: *(thinks)* I suppose because I wanted to have fun making other people laugh.

TANYA: Yeah, me too. It's great to share a laugh, isn't it?

BONZO: It's the nicest feeling in the world. But it's better if a special friend shares it with you.

TANYA: You're right.

BONZO: I mean, it's lovely to make strangers happy, but it's really great to share happy times with people you care about.

TANYA: Do you think that's why you couldn't smile?

Photocopiable

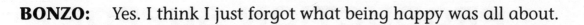

BONZO: Yes. I think I just forgot what being happy was all about.

TANYA: Having happy times with your special friends and family, you mean?

BONZO: That's right. Happiness makes you smile most when you share it like that.

TANYA: I'm glad you can smile again, Bonzo.

BONZO: So am I, Tanya. Thank you for helping me to smile again.

TANYA: You're welcome.

They both stand looking at each other and then smile and hug.

BONZO: Well, we'd better keep working if you're going to be as good a clown as me!

TANYA: Right! You're the boss!

BONZO: Let's try the smack over the back of the head with a plank of wood.

TANYA: Yeah, right. What do you think I was – born yesterday?

BONZO: *(laughs)* Oh, well, it was worth a try. Let's do the buckets of water instead, then.

TANYA: *(enthusiastically)* Yeah! I really love that one.

BONZO: Me too.

They continue practising their routine and can be heard laughing together as the lights fade to blackout.

A full circus show can be inserted here if you have the time and inclination!

THE END

Photocopiable

AUDITIONS AND CASTING

The easiest way to begin the audition process is to read through the play with the children two or three times.

The initial reading should be used to familiarize the children with the material. Allocate speeches, reading in sequence around the circle. In the second read-through, let the children volunteer to read specific character parts. In the third, nominate specific children to read certain character parts. During the second and third readings, encourage the children to think about using vocal expression, following the stage directions and picking up their cues quickly. Write yourself notes on how the children perform when reading specific roles. At every read-through, you must give each child a chance to read something.

It is important to make a concerted effort to allow less confident readers a chance to read, encouraging others in the group to show patience and consideration when listening. Plays always help poor readers to develop their language skills and their enthusiasm for performance often leads to a great deal of work away from rehearsals to ensure that they know their lines. A poor reader does not necessarily make a poor actor.

There are several alternative methods of casting your play, some of which are described below. The process can be as formal or informal as you wish.

FORMAL AUDITIONS
These can be held by selecting specific speeches or scenes from the play and asking the children to learn or recite them, or read them through, in various group combinations. The disadvantages of this method are

that it takes an inordinate amount of time to plan and execute, and it makes children very tense and often unable to perform well – especially if their memory skills are not strong.

CHILDREN CHOOSING THEIR OWN ROLES
Another option is to ask the children to write their first and second role choices, confidentially, on pieces of paper. Ask them to try and make sure the spelling is correct, and also to put their full names on the slips of paper. Some children will only have one choice of role, some will go for the same first choice, and there will be some children who 'don't care' what role they are given.

Gather all the pieces of paper together and, in a quiet place at another time, sit down and work out who wants what and which role combinations would work. Try to be as fair as possible, both to the children and to the play. Children are often aware of their 'failings' as actors, and usually accept that others have stronger performance skills, but this doesn't prevent many children from feeling acute disappointment if they fail to secure the role they are desperate for.

When allocating roles after using this method, sit the children in a circle and read from the bottom of the cast list upwards, giving the name of the character first and the name of the child who has been given that part after. Sometimes, a little of what is known as 'director speak' (see page 39) may be useful in trying to convince upset children that they are more suited to smaller 'character' roles than to a main part. After each part has been allocated, allow the children up to 5 minutes to discuss the casting and to accept and compare roles.

DRAWING NAMES OUT OF A HAT
Another method which is fairer, but more risky for your play, is to ask the children to put their names into a hat and to draw a name for each character. Children have mixed feelings about this process: there is always a possibility that their name will be drawn for the character they want to play, but they know that this is not very likely. Also, less confident children occasionally end up with large roles which they really don't feel happy or comfortable with performing.

CHOOSING ACTORS YOURSELF
The final option is simply to allocate the roles yourself, choosing children that you know are able and confident. However, this can upset children who are

rarely given the opportunity to perform, and removes any sense of the children being involved in the casting process.

After a number of years and a number of arguments, floods of tears and several very unhappy children, I have reached the conclusion that the second method is the fairest and surest option. This gives children a chance to specify which roles they would like to perform, and gives you the opportunity to make a final decision in a considered manner. It always surprises me which parts children choose to go for, and which appear to be the most popular! Sometimes children who appear confident – and who might have otherwise been given a major role – select small parts; likewise, children who appear less confident are keen to take on major roles.

It isn't strictly necessary to adhere to casting according to sex, either. Give females the opportunity to play male roles (and vice versa). The children will enjoy having the option of selecting a role because of what it is, and not being restricted because of what sex they are.

I feel very strongly that enthusiasm for playing their roles will result in an easier rehearsal process, an eagerness to learn lines and a willingness to throw themselves into the role wholeheartedly. I have been justified in this belief over and over again when 'risking' a major part on a child who may not have been given a chance to shine had I chosen a different method of casting.

Whichever casting method you have used, you should now ask the children to sit in a circle and arrange them according to character or family groups. Read through the play again together, to get the feel of how it sounds with all the roles established.

Finally, tell the children that each person in the cast is as important as the next; without any one character, you don't have a full team and, therefore, a complete play. They won't believe you – they've already spent time counting the number of lines they have to say – but it *is* true and needs to be expressed.

DIRECTOR SPEAK

Whatever decisions you make about casting, and however fair you try to be, there will be children who are upset when the parts are distributed. Many children feel that they never have the opportunity to show what they can do; some can build up quite a strong resentment against others who always seem to get the main roles, and quieter children can feel a sense of failure at not having pushed themselves forward yet again.

These feelings need to be dealt with as sensitively and as quickly as possible, away from the main group. In these situations you need to employ what is known as 'director speak' in an attempt to pacify, boost and reassure the children. This consists of using a variety of statements aimed to placate, such as:

● *I know you're upset about not getting the part you wanted, but I really needed a good actor like you for that scene to encourage all of the others to perform well.*
● *I understand that you wanted a main part, but you read this part so well that I just had to give it to you.*
● *I appreciate that you're disappointed, but I wanted to give you the chance to try something different this time, to show me what you can do.*
● *I realize that you might be a bit disappointed, but this character is very different from your own and will be a bit of a challenge for you, which I think you're ready for.*
● *I know that you're unhappy, but can you understand that I have to be fair to everyone and give others a chance to try a bigger part sometimes?*

And others of a similar nature. The children will probably recognize that you are trying to pacify them, but what is important about using 'director speak' is that you are hearing and acknowledging their feelings of unhappiness and that they have had the opportunity to express these feelings.

Whatever you say isn't going to make a lot of difference for some children. In these cases, they need to be given a straightforward choice between playing the part they have been given and not being in the play at all – however cruel that may seem. Most children will choose the former option. Any child opting out of the play should be kept occupied with other tasks, such as painting scenery, prompting or making props and costumes. They will often regret their decision to pull out and, if possible, should be given the chance to join in again.

The main aspect of the production of a play which is likely to anger and upset children is the part allocation. So if, when using 'director speak' on a previous occasion, you have promised a bigger part next time, you must fulfil that promise. Also, if you have stated that 'everyone needs to be given a chance' then do not under any circumstances allocate the main roles to the same children as were chosen last time.

Remember that all actors have fragile egos, and child actors are no exception. In selecting or auditioning for a role, they are putting themselves firmly in the firing line, exposing their wishes and asking you to praise their abilities, while all the time anticipating that they will get shot down. The worst thing you can do is to negate these feelings and ignore their insecurities. Even as an adult actor, I have felt upset at not being given a part I desperately wanted. These feelings can be magnified a hundred times for children.

Do not use 'director speak' simply to make life easier for yourself, even though it can help to create a positive working environment. I use it all the time and try to be reasonable, fair and understanding in the way that I use it. In that context, it works.

STRUCTURING REHEARSALS

When faced with directing a play, it is sometimes difficult to know what to tackle first. You have a large group of children awaiting your instructions, a limited amount of access to the school hall, and very little time! Good pre-rehearsal planning and preparation is therefore essential. The following timetable has always worked for me, and might also be useful for you.

PREPARATION
Immediately after casting, spend an hour or two resolving practical issues: what sort of stage the play will be performed on; how many entrances and exits the stage will have, and where these will be (plus a consideration of what imaginary setting lies beyond them if relevant); where the children will go when they are not on stage; exactly how and where each character enters and exits; what scenery, furniture and props you will have (if any), and where these will be positioned on the stage; whether any characters will enter from other parts of the auditorium and if so, where. All of these points need to be clearly defined to your own satisfaction before starting rehearsals.

REHEARSALS 1 TO 3
These should be used to complete what is known as 'blocking': simply specifying the movements of the children on, off and around the stage. Explain your staging ideas to the cast, marking out the stage area and exits with chairs. Tell them what furniture and scenery will be on stage, and use chairs or other equipment to represent this as well. Take time to ensure that all of the cast are familiar with the setting, the acting area and their movements, before continuing. They'll be desperate to get on with the 'acting', but it is essential that they understand the space they are working in, and know their own moves, before they try to go any further. It is impossible to teach children to act and give them instructions about where to enter and exit at the same time!

REHEARSALS 4 TO 8
Break the play down into small sections and rehearse these individually. Do not try to work through the whole play in a single rehearsal at this point. Start from the beginning and work through a maximum of three scenes. Rehearse the same section a number of times, until you feel that familiarity is beginning to reduce interest; then move on to the next section.

Continue the next rehearsal from where you left off last time; never repeat the previous section and then move on, or the result will be one or two sections that are absolutely brilliant and a number that are completely under-rehearsed! (I speak from experience!) This will mean that some children are unoccupied for some of the rehearsals. Set them learning their lines in pairs, watching the play and making notes, giving you feedback about how it looks, making props, designing posters and programmes, and so on. Insist that they remain aware of what is going on as they could be called into rehearsal at any time!

Carry on rehearsing the play in small sections until you have completed the whole script. Make notes as you go along of any potential difficulties; any scenes or characters which you feel will need extra rehearsing; and ideas that you have for scenery, props, costumes or effects.

REHEARSALS 9 TO 11
Use these rehearsals to concentrate upon scenes or sections which need extra attention. Try to get through the whole play at least once during each rehearsal period, but don't panic if you fail to do so!

Again, never go back over sections; always start the next rehearsal from the point at which you finished during the last one. Sections that have gone wrong should be repeated afterwards or at a later date, not straight away.

REHEARSALS 12 TO 14
These should be used for complete run-throughs: a technical rehearsal to go over any lights, sound effects, props or music you might be including, and two dress rehearsals complete with costumes and make-up. Spend 10 minutes at the beginning of the final rehearsal to work out and practise your 'curtain call', then run the play through completely without stopping.

Final rehearsals are always a nightmare – the children are stressed and excited, you're stressed and beginning to panic, and everyone seems to be snapping at each other!

Try to keep the children occupied at all times. Plan what you want to achieve in the rehearsals and try to stick to your plan.

I appreciate that this is the rehearsal structure for the 'ideal world', one which doesn't take into account those little things sent to try us: children being absent, cast members falling out, children not learning their lines and forgetting everything they learned at the last rehearsal, props and costumes failing to materialize... But those stresses are what give us the sense of achievement when the play finally goes on – and it *does* always go on, despite the horrendous feeling that it will fail. The old saying 'It'll be all right on the night' nearly always applies!

STAGING AND SCENERY

The Clown Who Couldn't Smile can be very simple to stage. It was first performed on a proscenium arch stage – a square, raised stage which resembles a box, with structured spaces at the side for 'wings' and full curtain. There was no set at all, the stage was completely bare and the children acted against a simple background of black curtains. Any props or furniture used was brought on and removed by the actors. The drawback of performing on a bare stage is that the children need to work that little bit harder in their acting to establish settings and create atmospheres.

The majority of characters simply walked on from the wings at the side of the stage to make their entrances, and exited in the same manner. All the sections of the stage were used to good effect. For example, during the circus acts, the clowns and acrobats used as much space as possible to demonstrate their skills.

The audience accepted the different settings in the play without the need for elaborate scenery and this play can work if performed simply against black curtains. The essential consideration if staging it in this manner is pace. Keep the entrances and exits swift, blending them as much as possible: when a character is leaving in one direction, a different character can enter from another. This provides enough variety to keep the audience interested without having to resort to creating elaborate scene changes.

Similarly, work hard to ensure that the scenes do not become too static in their use of space. Remember that actors do not have to restrict their entrances and exits to the stage area alone. You can create interesting effects, including audience diversion, by using other areas of the hall. However, if you want to be more adventurous and use scenery, there are a number of options open to you.

If the children are also performing on a proscenium arch stage, the solid back wall (known as the cyclorama, or cyc) can be decorated with fixed scenery that will be appropriate for most of the scenes in the play, or that presents a common theme. This could consist of painting a large 'big top' or simple striped canvas effect on the back wall. Alternatively, the 'general theme' idea can be taken one step further by decorating the proscenium arches themselves with a red-and-white-striped canvas 'tent' pattern and the cyc with a mural of a scene inside a circus tent, an external view of a circus tent, or vice versa. For the really adventurous, striped canvas could be draped from a central point above the stage to provide a cover to frame the performance and to give the impression that the actors are actually inside a circus tent – it is important to ensure, though, that this does not touch any of your stage lights and essential that it is made fire resistant prior to use. Any of these ideas would provide fixed scenery suitable for the majority of the scenes in the play.

Any scenery can be painted onto large sheets of lining paper or fabric and fixed to the arches to avoid permanent disfiguration. A similar process would work with the scenery attached to the cyc if it is also unfeasible to decorate that permanently. Just make sure that whatever you use to attach the scenery holds it on well!

If you are performing the play on a simple raised rostrum (as in many schools), you could create simple wooden or cardboard screens to act as the wings (on either side of the stage) and a back wall. These could be decorated with either the striped canvas effect, scenes from inside the circus ring, or an external view of the circus tent. Room dividers, or similar, are useful for this. Again, the screens can remain in place throughout the play, acting as a permanent backdrop for all the scenes.

If, however, you would like to change the scenery for each different setting you will obviously require some form of changeable backdrop. If you have a pulley system at your school, you can use it to hang painted backdrops. However, you are limited to the number of backdrops you can fit on a pulley system and so this method is not ideal. Other options include:

● Painting scenery onto large sheets of fabric and draping these over a long clothes rail (the type you find in warehouses or large stores). The rail can easily be swung round on castors to show the other side of any painted cloth, providing an instant scene change.
● Painting scenery onto large wooden or cardboard screens with castors attached, and wheeling these on to provide a moveable backdrop.
● Asking any potential carpenters to make a large wooden frame – approximately 8' × 6'. Attach a large piece of muslin or cotton to it firmly, then stretch the fabric tightly across and around the edge of the frame. Fix castors to the bottom, and paint your scenery onto

it. This can then be wheeled on to provide an instant backdrop. Fabric could be attached to both sides of the frame, providing two backdrops. The main problem then is moving these screens on and off the stage and storing them when they are not in use.

● Fixing a long, detachable pole across the back of the stage area and attaching several pieces of fabric, with a different scene painted on each one, in a 'flip chart' arrangement. The backdrops can then be flipped over as required.

● Using the same detachable pole, but drawing the fabric like a curtain across the back of the staging area. However, this will only provide one scenery change.

● If you are performing on a proscenium arch stage and have curtains at the back which can be drawn, these can be closed over any scenery painted on the cyclorama provide an instant change. It is essential, though, that someone remembers to open them again if you intend to have a 'grand finale' set inside the circus.

Whatever you choose, please remember two things:

● It is no great shame to select fixed scenery as an option. It is much better to spend what limited time and resources you have in creating a wonderfully elaborate setting that remains fixed, than to fail in trying to create a large variety of different scenery effects.

● Moveable scenery requires someone to be responsible for bringing it on and taking it off at the right times, and somewhere for it to be stored when not in use.

If your actors have to bring on and remove any scenery, furniture or props, ensure that everyone is clear about what they are responsible for and rehearse the scene changes as many times as you can. Audiences will forgive most things, but lengthy scene changes always cause them a great deal of irritation!

LIGHTING

Lighting in a play should be used to establish time, enhance setting or create atmosphere. If you are lucky enough to have a professional lighting rig, you can create some really wonderful lighting effects. If not, simple lighting can often be sufficient to establish the basics.

Our production of *The Clown Who Couldn't Smile* was lit very simply with what is known as a 'general wash' – the stage was flooded with light. The action could feasibly take place during the same day, reducing the necessity for elaborate time changes and allowing the lighting to remain constant throughout the play.

If you have the facility to dim or increase your lights, use this to good effect, especially for any performances of circus routines you might include. If you do not have the facility to change any of the lights, simply leave them all on for the whole play. Another option would be to borrow or hire some free-standing lights, which could be positioned at the side of the stage and used to create a 'theatrical' circus atmosphere.

If you have a professional lighting rig, you could use coloured gels to create some atmospheric lighting. These are transparencies which fit over your spotlights to give them a coloured glow. They have to be heat-resistant, and can only be purchased from a theatre lighting specialist. A couple of spotlights with blue, red and yellow gels attached, combined with a couple of clear, white spots will give an excellent 'showtime' effect if operated on an alternating sequence. If you do decide to create this effect by flashing coloured lights on and off in this manner, check first that your system will take it – some lighting rigs simply can't cope with being used in this way, and may explode.

We were fortunate enough to have access to professional spotlights for our production, but still kept the lighting extremely simple. Coloured gels on a few of the main stage lights gave the circus performances an interesting and colourful dimension. For the rest of the time, the stage was simply flooded with light – not subtle but effective. 'Blackouts' (extinguishing all lights) were used for scene changes and in preparation for the curtain call. For a stage with no front curtains, blackouts of this kind are useful, but make sure that your actors have practised moving around in the dark!

MUSIC AND SOUND EFFECTS

In our production of *The Clown Who Couldn't Smile*, music was used to create the circus atmosphere. Anything which reminds an audience of visiting the

The Clown
Smile

circus will work. I used a lovely, rousing march by Sousa as an introductory opener and repeated it for everyone to enter to during the curtain call at the end of the play. This then acted as a 'curtain', signalling to the audience when the play is starting and ending.

Slapstick music could underscore the clown act, which I kept very short. Many BBC sound effects CDs contain suitable silent-movie music which would work well in this context. Such CDs are widely available, but if you have difficulty finding one, use the 'Monty Python' theme music – itself a Sousa march – or anything similar.

Before using music in a public performance, check that your school has the relevant licences to broadcast music at a public event.

It isn't necessary to include any other music, or in fact any at all, if you prefer not to. However, it does create a lively circus atmosphere which provides an effective backdrop for BONZO's sadness. The clowns could perform their act to silence, but it is more interesting with a musical accompaniment. If you choose, other musical extracts could be included at various points during the play:

● Suitable music could be used to underscore the acrobats practising their routine at the beginning of Scene 3.
● BONZO could be given a sad song to sing at the end of Scene 6 as he sits alone on the hilltop. This could also be used to underscore other sad moments in the play prior to this (such as the end of Scene 3 or the end of Scene 5 – both are examples of BONZO exiting sadly).
● Different, appropriate, pieces of music could be included if you decide to produce a full circus show at the end of the play. Select one for each of the different circus acts who perform.

The use of other incidental music during the play is not recommended, although it could be interesting to use music as a character theme – playing the same tune each time a specific character enters. This would work particularly well with the character of MR BIG. However, this should really only be attempted with one or two characters and its use should be limited to avoid irritating the audience.

If, however, you want to include more music in your production of The Clown Who Couldn't Smile, make your selections carefully. The obvious choices are usually the best (for example 'Tears of a Clown'), but if you have the time, try to locate songs which reflect specific character's moods, as well as musical extracts which emphasize the general circus theme.

If you choose to include songs but do not want your actors to sing, other children in the school can

be utilized as a chorus. They can be seated around the staging area, singing the songs while those on stage mime appropriate actions.

Also, don't forget to utilize your talented school musicians – both teachers and pupils! The music doesn't have to be tuneful or played from musical scores. Interesting musical sound effects can be created with a variety of unusual or home-made instruments.

My big moment (as a teacher) in a school production was providing 'elephant' sounds on a baritone horn for a performance of The Jungle Book!

PROPS

Again, this play is very simple to stage. The only props (an abbreviation of 'properties') which could be included are:

● anything that might be used for the clown routine at the very beginning of the play, such as buckets, chairs, planks of wood, and so on
● chairs for the clowns to sit on (Scene 2)
● anything that might be used for the 'grand finale' of a complete circus act, if this is included.

Few of these items are actually essential, however. Many of them could be omitted or mimed. We did not use any props or furniture during the play at all as I preferred to create a clown routine which did not require props. This worked perfectly well, but if you have the time, a clown routine based around a single chair can be extremely funny. We did not include the use of chairs for the clowns in Scene 2 either, as the practicalities of bringing them all on and taking them all off would have been a nightmare! Too much furniture on the stage is simply a distraction to both your actors and your audience.

The essential point to remember with all props is: 'If it goes on, it must come off'. If an item makes its way onto the stage, then it must somehow make its way off again! Actors (of all ages) are notoriously bad at remembering this.

COSTUMES

The costumes for The Clown Who Couldn't Smile seem very difficult, but can be quite simple to organize. If you have the time and resources to create elaborate costumes based upon the circus theme, then feel free to do so. If not, the following ideas worked perfectly well for our production:

Clowns were dressed in brightly coloured trousers, shirts and T-shirts which we either found in charity shops, at jumble sales, or in the wardrobes of certain parents! We bought as many pairs of braces as we could to hold trousers up, and tied others around the waist with brightly coloured ribbon. The children wore the brightest shoes or boots that they possessed, threaded with coloured ribbons instead of laces, or simple black pumps which we decorated with coloured ribbon tied around the shoe and formed into a big bow. For those children wearing shirts with collars we added a colourful tie, or bright bow tie.

The children wearing T-shirts were given brightly coloured neckerchiefs or short scarves which could be simply made from strips of material. Battered hats in all manner of shapes and sizes completed the ensemble. The children wanted to wear 'clown wigs', but our budget wouldn't stretch to buying so many. If yours does, they are very effective and can be purchased from any good theatrical costumier or, occasionally, at larger joke shops. Don't worry if the only suitable 'clown' trousers you can find are too long – either roll them up or simply cut the legs down to size, as the 'tatty' effect will work well for these characters.

Charlie Chuckle was also given a horrendously patterned jacket found in a local charity shop.

The Strong Man was dressed in a fake leopardskin, sarong-type costume which joined on one shoulder, crossed over the chest, under the opposite arm and hung to just below the knees. It was made by a kind, talented parent and looked very effective. He had bare feet throughout the play.

Acrobats were all dressed identically in dark shorts and white vests with black pumps on their feet.

Lucinda wore a leotard with a skirt attachment to which we added a few diamante decorations on the front. She also wore matching tights and ballet pumps. Black plimsolls will work if these aren't available. We put her hair up in a beautiful bun decorated with bright ribbon.

Raymond also wore a leotard (but without the skirt!), tights and black pumps. We gelled his hair back to complete the look. (You need a very confident actor to wear this sort of costume on stage!)

Mr Big wore a black jacket and trousers, white school shirt, smart school shoes, dark socks and a black bow tie. If a black jacket is not available, a school blazer with the badge removed will suffice.

Children can be dressed in whatever modern outfits they feel comfortable wearing. Try to make a stereotypical distinction between males and females if you can.

Mrs Smith wore the brightest, most garish dress we could find. We combined this with court shoes, tan tights, a cardigan, a flowery hat and a handbag. All items were discovered in a local charity shop.

Aunty Val was dressed in a similar outfit to Mrs Smith, but slightly less colourful. She also carried a handbag and wore a hat.

Cousin Tanya was dressed in a clown's outfit (see above).

MAKE-UP

All make-up is dependent upon the type of lighting used in your performance arena. If you are working under professional stage lights, then more make-up needs to be applied, since they remove colour and contour from the face. However, if you are working under school lights or strip lights, be very careful just to define features and express the characters. Water-based make-up is best for whole face or body coverage; grease-based make-up is best for eye, cheeks and lips. Ensure that you make time to practise applying the make-up prior to the performances.

The make-up for *The Clown Who Couldn't Smile* is obviously extremely important, and its application very time-consuming. It is worth purchasing six cakes of water-based make-up in varying colours: white, red, green, blue, yellow and black (and possibly one other). Do not try to save money by buying smaller palettes containing a number of different colours – with a cast of this size you simply won't have enough.

Buy several good, small sponges and a few good quality make-up brushes. The other really useful item is a black eyeliner pencil (with sharpener), as this can be used for outlining the eyes and mouth – and for drawing moustaches on other characters. Both grease- and water-based make-up can be purchased from any good theatrical costumier's, and there are many specialist companies that provide a large variety of water-based face paints and theatre make-up.

Any base or foundation should be applied all over the face and neck area – including the ears and the back of the neck. A small amount of make-up must also be used to cover any other areas of bare flesh, such as arms and hands. For large expanses like these, water-based make-up is the fastest and most effective. It is important to cover all 'bare flesh' areas, especially if working under professional theatre lighting, as the lights will show very clearly the distinction between made up and non-made up flesh.

Water-based cake make-up, or face paints, need to be applied with a sponge which is barely damp and fully covered with make-up. If you have too much water on your sponge, the make-up will streak and application will be patchy. If you decide to use grease sticks to create a base or foundation, select a brick red (number 9 stick) and a colour paler than the child's skin. Apply the pale colour all over the face first, blending well with your fingers and then dot the red on the forehead, cheeks, chin and nose and blend this in thoroughly and carefully. The face should now have a good foundation base onto which you can apply other colours. If not, keep adding more of either colour, blending thoroughly until you are happy with the result. Use the same technique for all other areas of bare skin.

'Set' any grease make-up with a light dusting of loose powder to keep it in place under the hot stage lights. Take care when applying blusher using a grease stick as a little goes a very long way. Grease sticks for eye shadow come in a variety of colours (not just blue), and any of these can be used to make up your characters. It is a superstition, though, that green eye shadow is *never* worn in the theatre – you have been warned!

If you want to 'age' your children, use a red-toned grease stick and a cocktail stick. Ask the children to screw up their faces and apply the grease paint into the wrinkles using the cocktail stick. Think carefully about where wrinkles form on the face as you age, and draw them accordingly. Be careful not to draw in too many lines, or the poor child will end up with a face like a road map!

Try to avoid using ordinary make-up for the stage. It is not suitable and rarely withstands the heat, often fading within a few moments of being applied. Theatre make-up is specifically designed for the stage and it is worth spending £20–£30 on purchasing a good selection of proper theatrical make-up.

Other items which would be useful for your make-up box include: hair gel, talcum powder (for whitening hair), fake blood (mix glycerine with red food colouring), a stipple brush (or small blusher brush) and black grease stick for creating facial stubble, fake hair and spirit gum for applying it, cocktail sticks for creating age lines, teeth blackout liquid, coloured hair spray, glitter gels, and various coloured grease sticks.

Clown faces are a frightening prospect to make-up, but many good books can be found which will guide you through the process and give you ideas on design and application. If you have the time, the best idea would be to draw and colour your designs on paper first and then translate these to the make-up application. Tradition has it that each clown in existence wears his or her make-up in a completely different style to the others – no two clown faces are the same. This is fine if you have the imagination to do this, but do not worry if it is easier to give all of your clowns the same face!

Clowns: When it comes to applying the make-up, prepare all of the equipment in advance: sponges, bowls of water, brushes, towels, and so on. For each clown we used a white base which covered their face only. Set up a 'production line', with two or three willing helpers. The first person applies the bases, the second the eyes, and so on. If you have any older children assisting on your production, they can help with the clown make-up and often do this very well. Make sure you practise applying this make-up two or three times before the actual performance, as you always need more time for this than you anticipate. We painted the clown noses on, rather than use detachable ones as these fell off regularly and the children had difficulties speaking or breathing properly whilst wearing them! When all of the other face make-up was completely dry, we created bright red noses using a grease stick, so that they shone under the lights. This worked really well.

The Strong Man was given a light base of foundation, blue eye shadow, a slight touch of pale red blusher and pale red lips. We drew on a fantastic curly moustache using a black eyeliner pencil.

Acrobats wore the same base, eye shadow, blusher and lip colour as the Strong Man. These can be given curly moustaches, but they are not essential, and we didn't bother.

Lucinda was given a slightly darker base, blue eye shadow, slightly darker red blusher and bright red lips.

Raymond: Again, we used a darker base combined with blue eye shadow, a pale red blusher and pale red lips. He also had a fantastic curly moustache of black eyeliner pencil.

Mr Big was given a light base of foundation, blue eye shadow, a slight touch of pale red blusher and pale red lips. We also gave his nose a touch of red to indicate 'good living' and drew on a curly moustache. He was given a few 'age lines' to indicate his older (and wiser) status (see below).

Children: Make-up should be kept very light and simple. All of them need a little bit of foundation all over their face, with blue eye shadow, a touch of blusher and a pale red lipstick for boys, or a darker red or pink lipstick for girls.

Mrs Smith was given a light base, lots of blue eye shadow, a darker red blusher and bright pink lipstick (although bright red will work equally well).

Aunty Val was given similar make-up to Mrs Smith, but we toned it down slightly and gave her a different coloured lipstick.

Cousin Tanya and Charlie Chuckle were given clown make-up.

LEARNING LINES

Children never fail to amaze me with their capacity for learning and retaining lines. However, everyone needs support in learning lines at some time. Methods that can help include the following:

REPETITION

This requires constant and regular reading of the script. Go over the children's lines again and again, and they will learn them by rote. This method means that children often learn everyone else's lines as well – which is not a problem unless they start to prompt while on stage.

FROM CUES

Read the line immediately before theirs. Let the child read his or her line out loud. Read the 'cue line' again, but this time cover up the child's line on the script. This way, the children are learning the important cues as well as their own lines.

ON PAPER

Write each child's cue lines and own lines on a separate piece of paper, to prevent the children being daunted by a large script. Use this method for children to learn one scene or short section at a time. They can carry the pieces of paper around with them, and will memorize the lines quite quickly by absorbing these short extracts.

ON TAPE

Help the children to read through the script two or three times. Record each child's cue lines on tape, leaving a long pause after each one for the child to interject his or her own lines. Work through this with them initially, using the script as an accompanying visual aid; then let the children try it alone. Gradually remove their dependence on using the script, until they can say their lines in the recorded pauses on the tape without hesitating. Alternatively, you could record both the cue lines and the child's own lines, then leave a gap for the child to repeat his or her own lines. Either way, this method requires you to spend considerable time preparing the recordings!

VERBAL SUPPORT

Some children find it easier to learn lines by hearing them spoken and then simply repeating. However, this can take up an awful lot of your rehearsal time.

In addition, enlist the support of family members to help the children with their lines. Encourage children to 'test' each other, and try to create an atmosphere of support. Do not be too worried if the children paraphrase their lines, so long as important aspects of the script are not omitted.

Use what literacy time you can to read through the script a number of times as a whole group. Take a balanced approach: emphasize that the children need to remember what they have to say, but do not frighten them so much that they forget everything! Children should, however, be aware of the fact that they will not be able to take their scripts (or pieces of paper) onto the stage with them. This should be made clear as early in the rehearsal process as possible, to ensure that they all understand.

The most secure approach is to ensure that the children know (and if possible, learn) the whole script. This builds knowledge of what should happen in each scene, and means that the children can improvise or say another character's lines if something goes wrong. If you have the time, include within your rehearsal schedule one or two 'line-learn reheasrsals'. Sit with the children in a circle, positioning them in character order, then instruct them to recite the whole play with their scripts placed face down on the floor in front of them. This can help the person prompting to appreciate his or her job as well. It also helps your awareness of which children need more help with learning their lines.

Prompters should be instructed to give only the first word of a sentence, only supplying more words if the actor is still struggling. Ensure that only one person is responsible for prompting and give him or her every possible opportunity to practise.

It is also a good idea to tell the children a specific day by which they must have learned all of their lines. Tell them which rehearsal this will be – and stick to it! At that rehearsal, don't allow any children to go on stage with their scripts in hand. It will be a slow, painful process and the prompter will work overtime, but it is a necessary evil! Scripts are like security blankets: all actors panic when they are taken away. Try to intersperse these 'no scripts' rehearsals with additional 'line learn' rehearsals to boost the children's confidence.

A final note: never allow children to write lines on parts of their anatomy. A young girl of ten recently came to the dress rehearsal with her four lines written all over the palm of one hand. Even though they would have faded by the time the play went on that day, I very cruelly made her wash them off! Although she stumbled a little, she remembered her lines and felt a greater sense of achievement than she would have had if she had simply read them. It is not acceptable for actors to have lines written down anywhere on their person, or on pieces of paper anywhere on the stage. Children must realize this early in the rehearsal process. Apart from affecting the quality of the performance, it is also very risky – what happens if you lose your place while reading, the lines fade from your skin, or someone moves your piece of paper?

CALMING NERVES AND CHANNELLING ENERGY

Those children who become stressed and nervous about performing must be allowed to feel as if they have a 'get-out clause'. If possible, have another child in mind who can take over their lines and let them know that they do not have to perform if they really do not want to. I say this on a regular basis to the young children I direct; and however terrified they become, they always end up performing. I think this is because they know that taking part in the play is their choice, and that they can pull out at any time if they really want to.

Give the more 'energetic' (a euphemism for 'disruptive'!) children specific tasks to perform. I often involve these children in helping others to learn lines, in making props and even in applying make-up during rehearsals. Having a sense of responsibility about an important job will usually calm over-excited children. However, there is always the draconian option of threatening to remove them from the play – and meaning it – if they don't calm down.

The trick is to keep all of the children occupied. This prevents them from having time to be worried and uses up spare energy. Use your rehearsal planning time to add two or three production-related tasks that can be done whilst rehearsals are in progress. Alternatively, bring drawing paper and crayons to rehearsals and ask children to draw the stage and set. I've also used word puzzles, colouring books and asked children to write and decorate invitations to their families to come and see the play. All obvious strategies, but they work!

CURTAIN CALLS

I have seen some terrible curtain calls, that have completely spoiled an otherwise good performance. Bear in mind that this is the last memory your audience will have of the play, and that any sloppiness now will override any professionalism that has gone before.

I am not in favour of the pantomime-style 'walk-down' curtain call, where the actors come on to take their bows one by one (or in pairs), to the differing responses of the audience. In fact, I am completely against them. It must feel awful to have acted your heart out and then come on to take your bow to a lukewarm reception when your co-actor has just received a rousing, foot-stomping cheer! A good

way I have found of structuring my curtain calls is as follows:

1. Line up all of the children on stage in several rows according to height, with the tallest ones at the back. Space them out so that they can all be seen. (If they can see the audience, they can be seen.)
2. Tell the children to look around and notice who they are standing next to, in front of and behind.
3. Ask them to stand upright, with their feet together and their hands resting lightly on the front of their thighs.
4. Now nominate one child in the centre of the front row to start the bow. Tell all the other children to watch this child carefully, without making their observation noticeable.
5. When the nominated child on the front row bows slowly, everyone must bow. Bowing should be done from the waist, with hands sliding down to the knees and the eyes directed at the floor. Make sure everyone moves at the same, slow pace – bowing too quickly can give the appearance of a group of nodding ducks!
6. Tell the children to hold the bowing position for a slow count of two, then straighten up again.
7. Repeat, with everyone following the front row leader.

That is all that's required!

Finally – and essentially – make sure that the children maintain the same level of professionalism when leaving the stage. Don't allow them to scream, shout, wave to their parents or whatever! A smooth, professional ending like this can really round off a lovely performance.

For our production of *The Clown Who Couldn't Smile*, the children made their final appearance on the stage to a rousing Sousa march. They entered in groups of six and circled the stage, waving to the audience in true 'circus performer' style, until everyone was on. They then broke out of their circle to form their lines for the curtain call and the music was faded out. It made a very appropriate ending to the play and concluded it in style!

LITERACY SUPPORT

The following are some brief suggestions for literacy teaching that could follow on from reading and performing the playscript.

STORY

Ask the children to retell the story. This could be done in a number of ways:

● Groups retelling different sections in sequence, with the class as audience.
● Storyboarding the main events, with or without captions, in small groups or as a whole class.
● Record the main incidents in single sentences with accompanying pictures to create a 'wall story'.

Ask the children to devise an alternative ending for the play, continuing the story in scripted form and using the same style as the author. Then improvise and record it, in writing or on cassette.

CHARACTERS

Draw a picture of your favourite character. Explain to the rest of the class why this is your favourite. Then ask the children to draw their favourite character. Ask them to add the character's name at the top of their drawing and to write three words underneath the picture that describe the character's personality.

Ask the children who is their least favourite character and, in pairs, let them devise a conversation between the two, improvising the scene before recording it in writing or on tape.

THEME

Ask the children what they think the main theme of the play is (for example, the concept of happiness). They can work in small groups to improvise, and then write, a short play about the same theme. The plays can then be performed to the rest of the class. (These can be linked to the 'Happiness is...' freezes in Workshop Session 5 – see page 14.)

Ask the children to write a short, creative piece entitled 'Happiness is...' Use these pieces of work to explore metaphors and to devise metaphor poems.

WORKING WITH PLAYSCRIPT LAYOUT

Explore the layout conventions of playscripts, using a short section of the text. Look together at how stage directions are written, how the scenes are structured, and so on. Can the children explain these conventions?

Practise laying out a playscript on a computer, using a familiar story for content and the text of *The Clown Who Couldn't Smile* as a layout model.

PERFORMANCE-RELATED TASKS

Ask the children to:

● design a poster advertising a performance of the play, persuading friends and family to come
● design and draw the make-up for three of the characters in the play and explain their choice of colours. (This can be linked to the 'Clown faces' exercise in Workshop Session 4 see page 12.)
● design and draw the set for the first scene of the play, explaining and detailing their choices.